I've Seen Santa!

For my mum
–D.B.

For Andy, Caroline,
Charlotte, and Harry
–T.W.

ISBN 0-439-89533-2

Text copyright © 2005 by David Bedford.
Illustrations copyright © 2005 by Tim Warnes.
All rights reserved. Published by Scholastic Inc.,
557 Broadway, New York, NY 10012, by arrangement with
Tiger Tales, an imprint of ME Media LLC. SCHOLASTIC and
associated logos are trademarks and/or registered
trademarks of Scholastic Inc.

12 11 10 9 8 7 6 5 4 3 2 1   6 7 8 9 10 11/0

Printed in the U.S.A.   40

First Scholastic printing, September 2006

I've Seen Santa!

by David Bedford

Illustrated by
Tim Warnes

SCHOLASTIC INC.
New York Toronto London Auckland Sydney
Mexico City New Delhi Hong Kong Buenos Aires

It was Christmas Eve,
and Little Bear was looking
forward to seeing Santa.
"Is Santa as big as you?"
he asked Big Bear.

"Nearly," said Big Bear proudly.

"Oh," said Little Bear, looking worried.
"Will Santa fit down our chimney, then?"

"Of course he will!" said Big Bear. "I'll show you."

Big Bear went outside and climbed into
the chimney . . . .

CRASH!

"See?" said Big Bear, from a cloud of soot.
"Santa will get in, no problem!"

"Santa won't come if he sees this mess!"
said Mommy Bear.
"We'll help clean up," said Little Bear.

"Does Santa visit bears
all over the world?"
said Little Bear.
   "Yes," said Big Bear.
"He goes to every
   house."

"Hmm," said Little Bear. "He might not have time to come here, and then I won't have any presents."

"Don't worry," said Mommy Bear. "Santa will come just as soon as you go to sleep."

For SANTA
(paws OFF,
Big Bear!)

Little Bear didn't want to go to sleep.
He wanted to see Santa. He listened to
Mommy Bear and Big Bear going to bed.
And then... GLUG, GLUG, GLUG, GLUG

What was that noise?
Someone was downstairs!

Someone big was sitting
by the fireplace.
   "Yes!" whispered Little Bear.
"It's Santa! I've seen Santa!"
   Little Bear tiptoed up and saw...

Big Bear!

"That's Santa's milk!" said Little Bear.
"I only wanted a sip," said Big Bear,
"before I go to sleep." He took Little
Bear's hand. "Come on, Little Bear.
Let's go to bed."

Little Bear tried to stay awake, but he soon began to doze.

Then a loud noise downstairs woke him up.

MUNCH! MUNCH!

MUNCH! MUNCH!

Someone big was
standing by the
Christmas tree.
This time it had to be . . .

"You're eating Santa's blueberry pies now!" said Little Bear.

"I was hungry," said Big Bear.

"If Santa's as greedy as you," said Mommy Bear, coming downstairs, "he really WILL be too big to fit down the chimney! Now go to bed and go to sleep— both of you!"

Little Bear went to bed, but he couldn't go to sleep. He was too worried. He woke up Big Bear to ask him a question.

"What if Santa eats too many blueberry pies and then gets stuck in the chimney?" he whispered.

"Hmm," said Big Bear.

"Let's keep watch to make sure he's OK," said Little Bear. "We can hide so he won't see us."

"Shhh!" whispered Little Bear
from their hiding place.
"I can hear something.
It MUST be Santa this time!"

Someone was putting
presents in their stockings!
Big Bear turned on his
flashlight to see . . .

Mommy Bear!

"What are YOU doing?" said Big Bear.
   "I'm giving you both a present from me,"
said Mommy Bear. "What are YOU doing?"
   "We're not going to bed," said Big Bear.
   "We're going to see Santa!"
squealed Little Bear.

   Mommy Bear laughed.
   "Make room for me,
then," she said. "We'll
ALL see Santa."

Little Bear, Big Bear, and
Mommy Bear stayed downstairs
all through the night.

But they never did see Santa . . . .

even though
Santa saw them!

GOLF

THE ESSENTIAL GUIDE FOR YOUNG GOLFERS

KINGFISHER
LONDON & NEW YORK

Copyright © Kingfisher 2010
Published in the United States by Kingfisher,
175 Fifth Ave., New York, NY 10010
Kingfisher is an imprint of Macmillan Children's Books, London.
All rights reserved.

Consultant: Jason Muller

Photography by Dean Steadman

First published in hardback in 2010 by Kingfisher
This paperback edition publiched in 2013 by Kingfisher

With thanks to the Marriott Tudor Park Hotel & Country Club, Bearsted, Kent, U.K., and our models,
Anna Baker, Charlotte Copeland, Kira Elliott, Nicole Elliot, Mollie Lawrence, Toby Penniall,
Ben Scanlan, Jaskeerath Singh, Tavleen Singh, and Rylie Turner.
Thanks also to Titleist, FootJoy, and Cobra for kindly providing golf equipment.

Distributed in the U.S. and Canada by Macmillan, 175 Fifth Ave., New York, NY 10010.

Library of Congress Cataloging-in-Publication data has been applied for.

ISBN 978-0-7534-6809-8

Kingfisher books are available for special promotions and premiums.
For details contact: Special Markets Department, Macmillan,
175 Fifth Avenue, New York, NY 10010.

For more information, please visit www.kingfisherbooks.com

Printed in China
10 9 8 7 6 5 4 3 2 1
1TR/1212/UTD/WKT/128MA

Note to readers: The website addresses listed in this book are correct at the time of publishing.
However, due to the ever-changing nature of the Internet, website addresses and content can change.
Websites can contain links that are unsuitable for children. The publisher cannot be held responsible for
changes in website addresses or content or for information obtained through third-party websites.
We strongly advise that Internet searches be supervised by an adult.